Where Is Petey?

by Deborah Schecter

ISBN-13: 978-0-545-26009-1 / ISBN-10: 0-545-26009-4

Illustrated by Anne Kennedy
Designed by Maria Lilja • Colored by Ka-Yeon Kim-Li

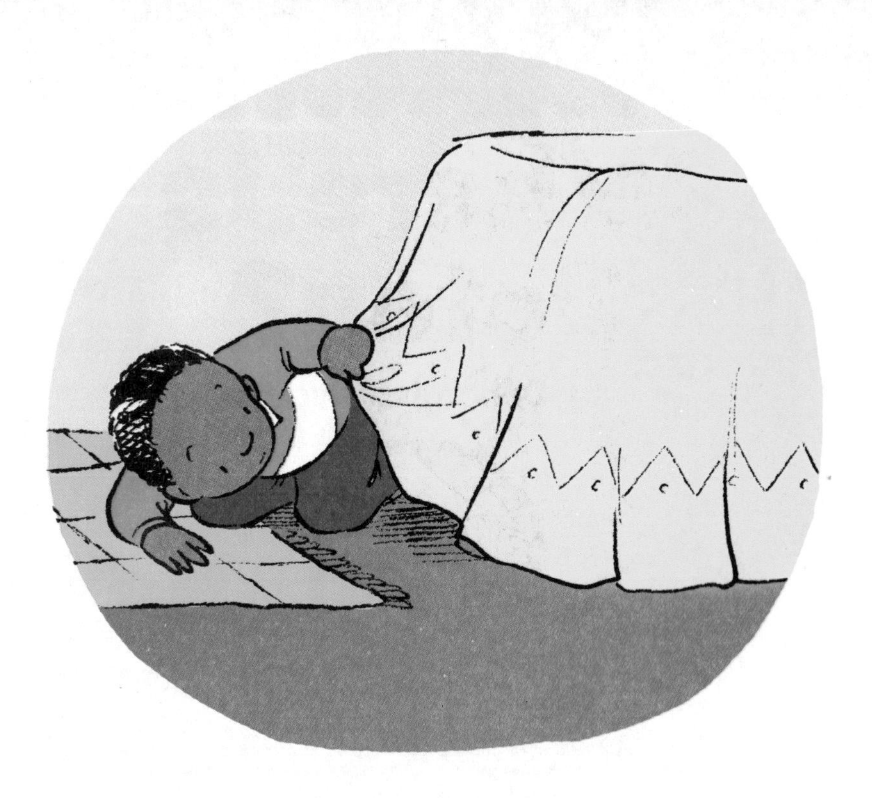

Where is Petey?
Is he under the bed?

Is he in the shed?

Is he behind the door?

Is he in the drawer?

Is he in the tub?

Is he under the rug?

Here is Petey!